G000230433

£6.99
UK only

This Annual belongs to Princess...............................

Editor: Sally Gilbert
Art Editor: Alexandra Brown
Photography: Colin Bowling

© Disney Enterprises, Inc. All rights reserved. Published in Great Britain in 2003 by Egmont Books Limited, 239 Kensington High Street, London W8 6SA. Printed in Italy.
ISBN 0 7498 5854 0

My

Disney's Princess Annual 2004

You shall go to the ball!

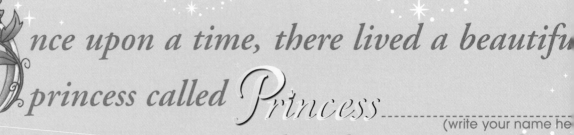

Once upon a time, there lived a beautiful princess called $\mathcal{P}rincess$ ----------

(write your name here)

One day, her Fairy Godmother appeared and declared, "You shall go to the ball..."

Beauty and the Beast Ball

8 *Invitation* **An invitation to read all about the ball in Paris**

9 *Beauty and the Beast Ball* **Learn all about the princess ball**

12 *Have a Ball!* **Quiz and puzzles about the ball**

14 *Beauty and the Beast* **Enjoy the fairy-tale story**

Princess Pampering and Preparation
Workshop One: Dressing-up

18 *Invitation* **Your invitation to the royal ball**

20 *Princess Gowns* **How to dress like the Disney princesses**

22 *How to Make a Ballgown* **Step-by-step guide to making your own gown for the ball**

24 *Princess Accessories* **Create two princess crafts for the ball**

26 *Princess Fashions* **Add a design to the gowns and colour in**

27 *Crowning Glory!* **Add a design to the tiara and colour in**

28 *Princess Style* **Complete our fashion quiz**

Workshop Two: Hair and Make-up

30 *Princess Hairstyles* **How to create a Disney princess hairstyle**

32 *Princess Hair Salon* **Fantastic hair tips and hairstyles to copy**

34 *Princess Make-up* **Step-by-step guide to make-up for a ball**

36 *Make-up Muddle!* **Complete our make-up puzzles**

37 *Ball Make-up* **Colour Snow White and Ariel's make-up**

38 *The Make-up Game* **Who will be the first to finish?**

Workshop Three: Dancing

40 *Once Upon a Dance* **Learn different dance styles**

42 *Dance Like a Princess* **Tips on how to dance daintily**

44 *Dancing Slippers* **Make dancing slippers for the ball**

45 *Dainty Dancer* **Complete our Snow White puzzle**

46 *Dancing Quiz* **Answer our dancing questions**

You shall go to the ball!

48 *Ball Checklist* **Final checks before you go to the ball**

50 *The Royal Ball* **The royal ball itself has arrived!**

56 *Life's a Ball!* **Plan and record your own ball**

60 *Ball Horoscopes* **Which princess sign are you?**

62 *Cinderella* **Read how Cinderella went to the ball**

66 *Cinderella Quiz* **Complete our Cinderella quiz**

67 *Ball Certificate* **Complete your own ball certificate**

69 *Competition*

Win a fantastic family break to

Now turn the page to discover your invitation...

Princess ....

You are invited to read all about the Beauty and the Beast Ball at **DISNEYLAND RESORT PARIS**

held on Saturday, 1st February, 2003

Beauty and the Beast Ball

Once upon a time, nearly two hundred competition winners from far and wide attended the Beauty and the Beast Ball in Disneyland Resort® Paris.

The day of the grand ball soon arrived. A royal itinerary was delivered to each and every princess. The itinerary invited everyone to take part in "Princess Pampering and Preparation" workshops, which would help the princesses to get ready for the ball. The princesses excitedly arrived at Disney's Hotel New York®.

In the first workshop, each princess was asked to choose a ballgown she would like to wear to the ball that evening.

A team of experienced seamstresses tailor-made each and every gown to each princess's specific requirements with pretty bows and corsages. As a final touch, each princess was given a glittering tiara to wear.

In the second workshop, the princesses were placed in front of a film-star style mirror, whilst having the finishing touches applied to their hair and make-up. They could choose their favourite colour face paints and

and courtiers amused the princesses. Then, the Court Herald announced the opening of the ball and invited the princesses to join him in the Grand Ballroom. As the princesses arrived, a royal fanfare greeted them and their names were announced to the other guests.

glitter, which was applied by their very own individual beautician.

The ballroom looked magnificent! There was a Beauty and the Beast ballroom backdrop and a spectacular water fountain

Finally, it was time to learn how to dance with elegance and grace. Everyone stood in a large circle and learnt a few dainty dance steps, taught to them by 'real' princes and princesses.
The evening of the royal ball soon arrived...everyone walked to the heart of Disneyland Park where it was to be held.

On arrival at the ball, royal jesters

in the middle of the dance-floor.
A grand orchestra started playing as the princesses entered the room. The room was decorated with balloons and flowers. In the centre of each table was an Enchanted Rose. Each guest was then handed a 'royal cocktail'.

into practice.

As the ball drew to a close, Belle and the Beast ended proceedings

Everyone was excited and knew they were in for an evening of fun and finery.

The Court Herald then announced the arrival of Mickey and Minnie Mouse. Dressed in their prince and princess outfits, they walked through the ballroom waving at everyone and took up their thrones on centre stage. Then Aurora, Snow White, Cinderella and their handsome princes arrived and greeted everyone. Last but by no means least, the guests of honour, Belle and the Beast arrived.

The Court Herald then announced the opening of the magnificent buffet, boasting the finest foods and drinks. After the buffet, the Disney princesses invited everyone to join them on the dance-floor and put the steps they had learnt earlier that day

with a romantic waltz. They then thanked each and every princess for attending. It was a truly magnificent ball and a wonderful time was had by all!

Have a Ball!

Now you've read all about the ball in Disneyland Paris, answer these questions about it, and solve the puzzles!

Royal Quiz

1) What were the Princess Pampering and Preparation workshops?

2) Who were the hosts of the ball?

3) Which Disney characters opened the ball?

Guest List

Can you unscramble these Disney princess names and discover who else attended the ball?

sonw hewit

icnedrlale

uarora

Answers:
Royal Quiz: 1) the Princess Pampering and Preparation workshops helped the princesses get ready for the ball 2) Belle and the Beast 3) Minnie and Mickey Mouse • Guest List: Snow White, Cinderella and Aurora.

Ball Wordsearch

How many times can you find the word 'ball' in the word grid below?

A	B	C	G	D	F	D	E	B	S	P	B	A	L	L	U	E	A	O	R
G	A	B	I	N	U	P	R	A	F	L	T	U	K	J	W	W	B	L	U
D	L	D	F	S	M	G	R	L	H	K	S	L	G	U	E	E	A	P	O
A	L	N	T	F	Q	O	N	R	O	M	A	D	O	D	R	R	L	F	F
G	S	J	B	A	L	L	E	P	N	N	L	B	A	L	L	T	L	D	D
H	U	K	P	I	S	G	S	F	V	B	L	G	S	I	Y	Y	Y	S	S
S	B	N	H	I	G	D	E	V	P	V	C	H	D	S	U	U	U	W	H
D	J	D	R	N	N	E	E	C	W	C	V	J	F	S	I	I	I	S	H

Charming Changes

There are six differences in the picture on the right. Can you spot them?

13

Beauty AND THE BEAST

This is the story of how Belle's life as a princess began...

Once upon a time, there lived a handsome, but very spoilt young prince. One winter's night, a poor old woman came to his castle, hoping the prince would offer her shelter from the cold.

"You are old and ugly," said the prince. "Go away!"

"Don't be fooled by appearances," the woman said. "Beauty is found within."

With these words, the old woman turned into a beautiful enchantress. To punish the prince, she turned him into a horrible Beast and cast a spell on all of his servants in the castle, too. The enchantress left the prince with a rose that would stay in bloom until his twenty-first year. I the prince could learn to love another, and have his love returned before the last petal fell, the spell would be broken. If not, he would remain a Beast for ever!

Not far from the castle was a little village. A beautiful, kind girl named Belle lived there and she loved to read books. Gaston, the mos handsome man in the village, wanted to marry Belle, but she didn't share hi affection. Belle dreamed of faraway

places and romance – not of Gaston.

One day, Belle's father, Maurice, who was an inventor, set off on his horse, Phillipe, to attend a fair where he would display his latest inventions. As he travelled through the dark woods, he became lost and frightened. Soon he came across the Beast's gloomy castle. The castle scared Phillipe and he threw Maurice off and galloped away leaving the old man alone. The Beast jumped out and grabbed Maurice. He brought Maurice to the castle and locked him in a cold, dark dungeon.

Meanwhile, Phillipe returned to the village to get Belle's help. She travelled to the castle and offered herself as prisoner to the Beast if he released her father. The Beast accepted and chased Maurice away.

Belle found it very difficult living in the castle at first. However, she soon became friends with the Beast's servants, who made her feel very welcome, for she was their only chance of becoming human again. Over time, they could see that Belle and the Beast were falling in love.

The very night that the Beast decided to declare his love for Belle, she told him how she longed to see her father again. The Beast loved Belle so much

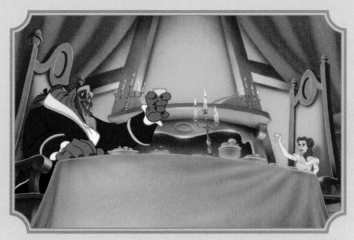

that he set her free.

When Belle returned to the village, she learned that Gaston was planning an attack on the Beast. Belle and her father bravely went back to the castle to warn the Beast... but it was too late. Gaston shot the Beast and he fell to the ground.

Belle rushed over to the Beast. She knelt beside him and confessed her love for him just as the last petal fell from the Enchanted Rose. Suddenly, a flash of light surrounded the Beast. At last, true love had

broken the enchantress's spell. The Beast became a prince again and the enchanted servants were suddenly human once more! The magic light brought Belle and the prince into the ballroom where they danced the first of many dances in their life together. And they all lived happily ever after!

The End

To her royal highness,

Princess ....
(write your name here)

You are invited to a princess ball at the royal palace

Dress code: Tiara and ballgown

Turn the page for your Princess Pampering and Preparation Workshops...

Princess Pampering and Preparation

Workshop One:

Dressing-up

Princess Gowns

Being invited to a ball is very exciting! The first thing to think about is what to wear. Read how to look just like your favourite Disney princesses!

Belle

- Gather lengths of yellow crêpe paper to make a skirt.

- Wrap yellow crêpe paper around the body and white around your waist, and secure.

- Wrap crêpe paper around your shoulders and cross in front. Tape in place.

Mulan

- Place a flower accessory and hairband in your hair.

- Put on a Chinese-style night dress or top.

- Place a flower bracelet around your wrist.

Jasmine

- Wear pink or purple pyjama bottoms and a bikini top.

- Make a beaded belt to wrap around your waist.

- Wear a headband in your hair.

Aurora

- Put on a pretty, pink party dress.

- Wrap a pink shawl over your shoulders.

- Wear princess slippers on your feet.

21

How to Make a Ballgown

Follow our step-by-step guide to creating your own gown and you'll be the prettiest princess in the ballroom.

You will need

white and pink netting

wide ribbon

safety pins

leotard

flowers and
sequinned patches

stapler and staples

glue

scissors

 1 Put on a leotard. Cut a length of white netting and staple into pleats. Repeat this and pin the lengths of netting on to the leotard in a skirt shape.

2 Cut a length of pink netting and staple into pleats. Repeat this with more lengths. Place the pink netting over the white netting and fasten with a pin.

♥ A princess wearing her ballgown at the Beauty and the Beast ball!

3 Tie a ribbon around your waist in a bow. Decorate the skirt by sticking on flowers and sequinned patches.

23

Princess Accessories

Accessories can add the finishing touch to your gown. Make this tiara and bracelet - they are fit for any ball!

Glitter Tiara

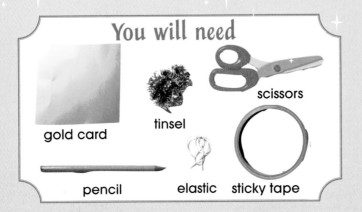

You will need

gold card

tinsel

scissors

pencil

elastic

sticky tape

1

Draw a tiara shape on to gold card and carefully cut out.

2

Cut lengths of tinsel and tape on to your tiara in a pretty design.

3

Cut a length of elastic and tape to the back of your tiara on both sides.

Princess Fact!
Now you are dressed for any ball!

Glitter Bracelet

1 Cut a strip of gold card to go around your wrist.

You will need

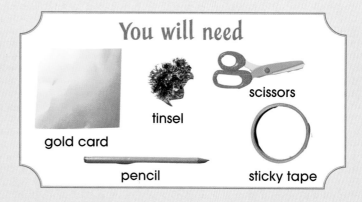

gold card

tinsel

scissors

pencil

sticky tape

2 Tape the strip of gold card into a bracelet shape.

3 Decorate the gold bracelet by winding a length of tinsel around it. Tape in place.

Princess Fashions

Add your own designs to these gowns and then colour them in.

Crowning Glory!

Now, colour this tiara. Try adding some glitter glue or coloured paper for extra princess sparkle.

Princess Tip!
If you need any more, trace off the patterns and colour them in yourself.

Princess Style

Complete this quiz to see which princess has the same fashion style as you.

1) Which is your favourite colour?
a) Yellow
b) Purple
c) Pink
d) Green

2) You are going to a ball. What would you choose to wear?
a) An off-the-shoulder gown
b) A smart trouser suit
c) A full-skirted gown
d) A bikini and a floaty dress

3) Which accessory would you prefer to wear?
a) Gloves
b) Jewelled headband
c) Gold tiara
d) Seashell necklace

4) How would you describe your style?
a) Romantic
b) Exotic and elegant
c) Classic
d) Fun

Mostly a

Like Belle, you love to wear romantic gowns. A pair of elegant gloves make sure you are the belle of the ball.

Mostly b

Your favourite style is exotic. Like Jasmine, elegant trousers are your first choice and reflect your adventurous side.

Mostly c

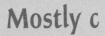

You love wearing classic, simple styles, just like Aurora. You finish off your look with gold accessories.

Mostly d

Like Ariel, you have your own individual fashion style. You like soft, shimmering fabrics and seashell accessories.

Princess Pampering and Preparation

Workshop Two:

Hair and Make-up

Princess Hairstyles

You'll be the belle of the ball with these pretty princess hairstyles!

Belle

To create Belle's hairstyle, lift up the side sections of your hair and secure in a clip. Finish with a sparkling tiara or pretty hairband.

Pocahontas

To create a Pocahontas hairstyle, brush your hair until it shines. Then brush behind one ear and let the rest of your hair cascade over your shoulder.

Jasmine

To create Jasmine's hairstyle, pull your hair back into a loose ponytail and secure with a ribbon. Add another ribbon further down the ponytail and a gold jewelled headband.

Aurora

To create Aurora's hairstyle, try sleeping in plaited hair. Take the plaits out in the morning, then ask an adult to curl the ends with a hot brush. Finally, add a glittering tiara!

Cinderella

To create Cinderella's hairstyle, tie your hair into a high ponytail. Wrap the ponytail around a hairband to form a bun. Place a blue headband over your head.

Snow White

To create Snow White's hairstyle, brush your hair until it gleams. Take a piece of red ribbon and tie it into a bow on the top of your head.

Princess Hair Salon

Step into the princess hair salon and pick up some top tips!

Party Hairstyle

To create our princess party look, take small sections of hair and plait them, securing with a pretty hair accessory.
You can add hair glitter and hair mascara to make it look special.

Final touches to a princess's hair at the Beauty and the Beast ball!

Classic Hairstyle

To create our classic hairstyle, wash and brush your hair. Let your hair dry naturally and hang over your shoulders. To finish, simply tie a pink ribbon into your hair.

Another glamorous princess hairstyle at the ball!

Princess Hairstyle Tips

❤ Wash your hair until it squeaks to make sure it is really clean.

❤ Let your hair dry naturally rather than using a hairdryer to keep it in good condition.

❤ Always try and make sure your hair is clean, neat and tidy.

❤ Do not use rubber bands to tie your hair back, as they will cause it to break.

❤ For coloured streaks, try some coloured hair mascara. It's easy to use, looks great and washes out easily!

❤ Wear a shower cap in the bath or shower to prevent your hair looking frizzy.

❤ Hair-clips look great in long or short hair and add lots of princess glamour.

Princess Make-up

Follow our step-by-step guide to princess make-up and read our helpful tips, too!

Party Make-up

Tie your hair back and clean your face.

Choose a make-up colour and apply in wavy lines.

Add more lines and spots in other colours.

Stick on body jewels and apply face glitter.

Natural Make-up

When it comes to wearing make-up, sometimes less is more. Remember, brush lightly with powder for the day – a touch of lip gloss is all you need. Try sparkle for the ball.

Make-up Tips

- 💜 **Always wash your make-up brushes and sponges.**

- 💜 **Remember to remove all make-up before you go to bed.**

- 💜 **Face paints are available in most good toy shops.**

- 💜 **Wear something old when you are putting on your make-up in case you make a mess.**

- 💜 **Use foundation first for lipstick that lasts until midnight!**

- 💜 *A princess having her make-up applied for the ball.*

Make-up Muddle!

Every princess knows the importance of make-up. Complete these puzzles to finish Cinderella's make-up.

Odd One Out

Can you spot the odd one out?

Answer: The hairbrush is the odd one out, as all the others are items of make-up.

Mirror Image

Which shadow matches the mirror?

a

 c

b

 d

Answer: Shadow b matches the mirror.

Make-up List

Fill in the missing letters to complete the list of make-up you need to apply before you go to the ball.

Lip__ick

Blu__er

E__shado_

M__cara

Answer: Lipstick, Blusher, Eyeshadow, Mascara.

36

Ball Make-up

Help Snow White and Ariel apply their make-up before they go to the ball. You can copy their make-up or use your princess imagination!

The Make-up Game

Who will be the first to apply their make-up - Ariel, Jasmine or Esmeralda? Play this game to find out.

How to play: Trace or cut out the princess counters. Place each princess on her coloured starting place, then take it in turn to throw a dice for each one and move her forward the correct number of places. Each time the princess gets back to her staring place, colour one of her items of make-up. The first princess to colour all her make-up is the winner!

Princess Pampering and Preparation
Workshop Three:
Dancing

Once Upon a Dance

*All the Disney princesses love to dance.
Have a look at the different types of dance
they like to do.*

Dancing in the Street

Esmeralda loves to dance for
other people. You will often
find her dancing in the street,
shaking her tambourine. Djali
likes to join in, too!

Ballroom Dancing

Belle and the
Beast enjoy
ballroom dancing
because it is
romantic.

Woodland Waltz

Aurora and Prince Phillip like dancing in the woods so they can dance with all the woodland creatures.

Exotic Dancing

Jasmine likes to experiment with exotic dancing. She often uses silk scarfs to add more movement. She can belly dance, too!

Ribbon Dance

Mulan favours a traditional Chinese dance, the ribbon dance! It is very dramatic and beautiful.

Dance Like a Princess

You don't have to be a wonderful dancer to attend a ball. However, you will need to practise hard and learn some dance steps beforehand.

Dancing Tips

- Check the floor where you are going to dance is clear.

- If you are using CDs or cassettes for music, you may need someone to be your sound engineer and play the right tracks when someone signals, or 'gives the cue'.

- Wear a pretty gown that will flare out as you spin around.

- Wear sensible shoes, otherwise you may have an accident.

- Be as graceful as a drifting breeze.

- Point your toes as you walk across the dance floor.

- Try not to step on your partner's toes.

- Smile, and enjoy yourself.

- Let yourself go to the music.

The Waltz

The waltz is the legendary dance of romance. Flowing and graceful, every girl feels like a princess as she floats around the floor to beautiful waltz music.

Dance Steps

 1 Stand up straight with your feet together.

 2 Step forward with your right foot (count 1).

 3 Step forward with your left foot (count 2) and put your right foot next to your left (count 3).

 4 Step back with your left foot (count 1).

 5 Step back with your right foot (count 2) and put your left foot next to your right (count 3).

 6 Repeat these steps and move in different directions around the room.

The Jive

Jiving is a very energetic rock and roll dance from the 1950s. Do it with a partner. Hold hands and swing around, twist under one another's arms and shake your hips in time to the beat.

How to curtsey

At the beginning of a dance it is always polite to curtsey to your partner.

- Move one foot behind the other.

- Take the hem of your skirt or dress in your hands.

- Bend at the knees, bowing your body towards your partner. At the bottom of your curtsey, pause for a moment, remaining bent over towards your partner.

- Now, as you rise, lift your hem with you.

Dancing Slippers

All princesses need dancing slippers if they are attending a ball. Here's how to make your very own pair.

You will need

gold card   netting   pumps   sticky tape

pencil   fabric flowers   scissors

1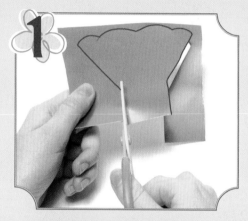

Draw a shape for each shoe on to gold card and cut out.

Princess Tip!
In step one, make the shape long enough so it can be folded into your shoe.

2

Tape pleated netting and flowers on to your gold shapes.

3

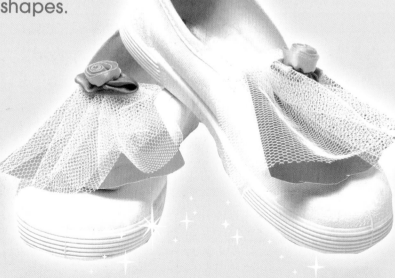

Tuck and tape the end of each shape inside both shoes.

Dainty Dancer

Snow White is learning a new dance routine. Help her complete each sequence by drawing the correct picture from the bottom of the page into the numbered space.

Copy Snow White's movements and you can dance like a princess, too!

45

Dancing Quiz

How well did you read the princess dancing section?
Complete these questions below to find out.

1 What is a waltz?_____

_____

2 How do you do a curtsey?

_____

_____

3 Write down two dancing tips...

_____

_____

_____

4 What is Belle and the Beast's favourite type of dancing?

_____

5 What does Mulan use to help her dance?

_____

6 What is the name of the energetic rock and roll dance from the 1950s?

_____

Princess Tip!
If you can't remember the answers to all these questions, go back to page 40.

To her royal highness,

Princess..................................
(write your name here)

You shall go to the ball!

Ball Checklist

You're nearly ready for the ball. Before you leave, complete this checklist so you don't forget anything.

Ball Checklist

You have replied to the invitation	☐	You have a gift for the hostess	☐
You are wearing your favourite ballgown	☐	You've arranged the carriage so you can arrive in style	☐
You are wearing your favourite accessories	☐	You have taken your camera with you	☐
Hairstyle and make-up are perfect	☐	You have practised your curtsey	☐
You are wearing a tiara	☐	You have your handbag	☐
Dancing slippers are sparkling	☐	You have your invitation	☐
You know your dance steps off by heart	☐	Finally, check your make-up before your leave and make your grand entrance	☐

Notes

_____
_____
_____
_____
_____
_____
_____
_____
_____

Princess Ball Tips

Cinderella says, "There is a tiara for every occasion."

Belle says, "Match your shoes and your handbag."

Snow White says, "Your best make-up is your smile."

Aurora says, "Make sure your tiara complements your gown."

The Royal Ball

The evening of the royal ball has arrived! Your glittering carriage pulls up outside the palace. The coachman takes your hand and helps you down from the carriage. You walk up the palace steps with your invitation in your hand.

Ball Invitation

Follow these easy steps to make your own ball invitations.

1 Draw tiara and palace shapes on to colourful card.

2 Carefully, cut out the tiara and palace shapes and write on the back.

At the entrance to the ballroom, the Court Herald announces your arrival.

Guest List Scroll

Follow these simple steps to make your own Court Herald scroll, so you can announce the guests' names at your next ball.

1 Tape two pieces of paper together lengthways and glue a ribbon along the back.

2 Write your guests' names on the inside of the scroll.

♥ *The Court Herald announcing guests at the ball*

Soon, a royal trumpet signals the beginning of the ball.

Royal Fanfare

Here's how to make a royal trumpet for your ball.

1 Cover the inside tube of a roll of kitchen foil with gold paper.

2 Make a princess flag and attach to the gold tube with cord.

The banqueting hall is full of the most scrumptious foods and drinks!

Coach Cakes

Here's a simple recipe so your own guests can dine like princessess.

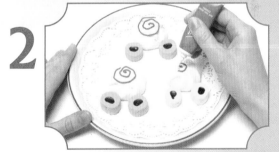

1 Place three meringes on a plate and add liquorice sweets for the wheels.

2 Decorate each meringue by making a swirl with red icing.

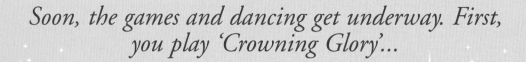

Soon, the games and dancing get underway. First, you play 'Crowning Glory'...

How to play Crowning Glory

Place a picture of a princess on a wall. Each player then takes it in turn to wear a blindfold and place a paper crown on her head. The player that places the crown nearest the princess's head wins!

...then you play 'Pass the Tiara'...

How to play Pass the Tiara

Sit in a circle, facing each other. Put on some music and pass a tiara round the circle. When the music stops, the player holding the tiara is out. The last person in keeps the tiara.

...then you join in with 'Kiss the Prince'...

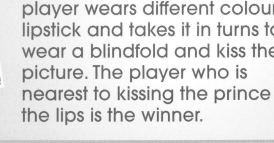

How to play Kiss the Prince

Place a picture of a Prince Charming on a wall. Each player wears different coloured lipstick and takes it in turns to wear a blindfold and kiss the picture. The player who is nearest to kissing the prince on the lips is the winner.

...next, it's 'Musical Thrones'...

How to play Musical Thrones

Set out some chairs and one throne back-to-back in a row. Dance around the chairs to some music. As the music stops, find a chair to sit on. When it starts, take one chair away. When it stops again, any player without a chair leaves the game. Carry on until only the throne is left. The player sitting on the throne wins!

Turn the page to see what game you play next...

How to play the Lost Slipper game

Each person takes off one shoe and places it in the middle of the room. Everyone covers their eyes while Drizella and Anastasia, Cinderella's evil stepsisters, hide the shoes. The person to find the most shoes is the winner.

then you play Pin the Star on the Fairy Godmother's Wand...

How to play Pin the Star on the Godmother's Wand

Draw a picture of a Fairy Godmother holding her magic wand. However, don't draw the star on the tip of the magic wand. Draw and cut out enough card stars for each of your guests. Write the name of each guest on a star. Attach a rolled piece of masking tape on the back of each star. Blindfold each guest and turn them around three times. With star in hand, point the guests in the direction of the Fairy Godmother. The winner is the guest who places their star nearest to the end of the Fairy Godmother's magic wand.

After the games have finished you dance into the night...well, at least until the clock strikes midnight!

As you leave the ball, you are presented with a princess gift bag. You thank your host for a truly enchanting evening.

Princess Gift Bags

Make these pretty gift bags whenever you host a ball for your guests to take home afterwards.

You will need

coloured netting

scissors

tinsel

sweets

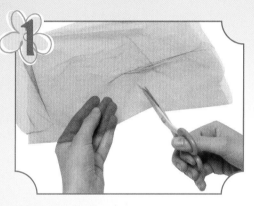

1 For each parcel, cut two squares of netting. Use two different colours if you have them.

2 Place one square on top of another and place some sweets into the centre.

3 Gather the netting and tie a piece of tinsel or string around to close.

When you reach home, you smile to yourself remembering the wonderful evening you had at the royal palace ball!

Life's a Ball!

After you attend a ball it is polite to return the favour. Use the ideas and tips you have read so far and plan your own ball below. Then, record how the ball went on the following pages.

Ball Planner

Theme of ball

_____

_____

_____

_____

Date

_____

Guests

_____

_____

_____

_____

Location

_____

_____

My outfit

My accessories

Food and drink

Games

Record of your Ball

When was your ball?

How many people did you invite?

How many people attended your ball?

What games did you play?

What food and drink was there?

What did your guests say about the ball?

Did your ball have a theme?

_____

_____

In the space below, draw a picture of your ball.

Ask your guests to sign their name below to show they attended.

_____

_____

_____

_____

Ball Horoscopes

Read our ball zodiac signs. Find out which princess you share a star sign with and what type of ball you are mostly likely to host.

Aquarius
21 January - 18 February

Like Pocahontas, you would host an outdoor ball. You love playing outdoor games and dancing to the songs of the wind.

Pisces
19 February - 20 March

You and Ariel would ask everyone to wear pretty beach wear. You would have fun playing lots of beach games.

Aries
21 March - 20 April

Just like Esmeralda, you are a lively person. You would host a ball with lots of dancing, entertainment and party music!

Taurus
21 April - 21 May

You are just like Tinker Bell. You would host a truly magical ball which would make everyone's dreams come true.

Gemini
22 May - 21 June

You and Cinderella share the same views on what makes a grand ball. You would ensure that everyone is dressed up to the nines!

Cancer

22 June - 22 July

Like Aurora, you enjoy surprise balls. You would probably host a ball in the woods, so all your woodland friends could attend.

Leo

23 July - 23 August

You are traditional, like Snow White, and would host a simple ball. The food would be home-cooked and your decorations home-made.

Virgo

24 August - 22 September

You are just like Melody and would opt for a beach-front ball. There would be plenty of ice-creams for everyone!

Libra

23 September - 23 October

You and Jasmine would both love to host a ball in an exotic location. You would opt for adventurous party games and food.

Scorpio

24 October - 22 November

You are quirky and fun, just like Alice. You would host a splendid fancy dress ball and play lots of unusual party games.

Sagittarius

23 November - 22 December

Like Mulan you would host a Chinese ball with traditional dancing, decorations, music and food.

Capricorn

23 December - 20 January

You are just like Belle. You would host an intimate ball in a pretty ballroom with only a few choice friends. Romance is also a key factor at your ball!

Cinderella

This is the story of how one princess went to the ball...

Once upon a time, in a faraway land, there lived a widowed gentleman and his beautiful daughter, Cinderella. He soon married again so that his daughter would have a mother to care for her. The woman he married had two daughters of her own, Anastasia and Drizella.

Sadly, Cinderella's father died soon afterwards, leaving her alone with her stepmother, Lady Tremaine, and her two stepsisters. Anastasia and Drizella hated Cinderella and so did their mother. They soon made her into a servant in her own home.

Cinderella quickly discovered her only true friends were the birds and mice. They would often listen as she sang about her dreams of life filled with love and happiness.

One day, a royal messenger delivered a sealed envelope to the house. It was an invitation to the palace ball. When Cinderella asked her stepmother if she might go to the ball, her stepmother agreed, on condition that Cinderella finished all her chores and had something

to wear.

Cinderella rushed to her bedroom excitedly to start work on her ballgown. No sooner had she started than her stepsisters gave her a lot of extra work to do. The mice knew that Cinderella would never have time to finish her dress, so they decided to work on it themselves.

At last, the dress was finished. When Anastasia and Drizella saw their stepsister looking so beautiful they were filled with jealousy and ruined the dress.

Cinderella ran into the garden and wept. She was so upset that she did not see her Fairy Godmother appear before her.

In a flash, the Fairy Godmother waved her magic wand and transformed a pumpkin into a glittering carriage, the mice into four white horses, Cinderella's horse into a coachman, and Bruno the dog into a footman!

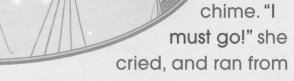

Then, with a final wave of her wand, Cinderella was dressed in a beautiful ballgown and glass slippers.

Cinderella thanked her Fairy Godmother as she stepped into the carriage. "Remember...at the stroke of midnight...the spell will be broken," warned the Fairy Godmother.

At the ball, the prince danced with Cinderella all night long. Everyone at the ball, especially Lady Tremaine and the stepsisters, wanted to know who the mystery princess was.

Cinderella was so happy she forgot all about the Fairy Godmother's warning.

Suddenly, the clock began to chime. "I must go!" she cried, and ran from the palace. As she ran down the palace steps she lost one of her glass slippers.

On the last stroke of midnight, everything returned to the way it was before...apart from the single glass slipper.

Back at the palace, the prince found the glass slipper and declared that he would only marry the girl it fitted.

The next day, the Grand Duke visited every maiden in the land in search of its owner. The stepsisters tried to squeeze their feet into the slipper, but their feet were too big.

Meanwhile, Lady Tremaine had locked Cinderella in the attic as she suspected that she might have

something to do with the mystery princess at the ball. It was only when Jaq and Gus, the mice, freed Cinderella

and she announced herself to the Grand Duke that she was given the opportunity to try on the glass slipper.

As the footman stepped forward, Lady Tremaine tripped him up. The slipper fell to the floor and shattered into a thousand tiny pieces.

"Maybe this will help," said Cinderella, as she revealed the other glass slipper from her pocket and tried it on. Of course, it was a perfect fit!

Soon afterwards, Cinderella and her prince were married. Her friends smiled, as they knew Cinderella's dreams had finally come true!

The End

Cinderella Quiz

You've read the Cinderella story, but how much have you remembered? Answer these questions to find out.

1 Who helped Cinderella go to the ball?
_____

2 How did Cinderella arrive at the ball?
_____

3 Who did she dance with?
_____

4 What time did she leave the ball?
_____

5 What did she lose as she left the ball?
_____

6 What happened on the last stoke of midnight?
_____

7 How did the Grand Duke know Cinderella was the mystery princess from the ball?
_____

8 Who did Cinderella marry?
_____

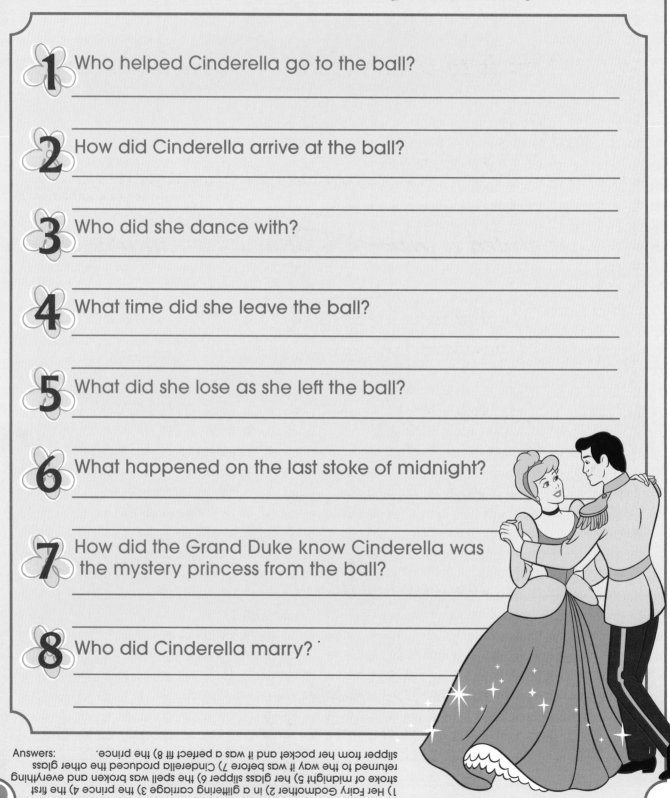

Answers: 1) Her Fairy Godmother 2) in a glittering carriage 3) the prince 4) the first stroke of midnight 5) her glass slipper 6) the spell was broken and everything returned to the way it was before 7) Cinderella produced the other glass slipper from her pocket and it was a perfect fit 8) the prince.

Ball Certificate
Congratulations!

This is to certify that her royal highness

Princess ....

attended a princess ball at the royal palace.

- *You were dressed to dance the night away*

- *You looked as beautiful as a true princess*

- *You danced like a dream*

- *You were the belle of the ball*

More Disney fun in these great magazines...

FREE Lion mask!

Disney and Me

Colouring!

Fun!

Puzzles!

On sale every fortnight

Where all your Disney friends come to play!

Enter the magical world of princesses!

Free Pretty necklace!

Issue 61
12 February - 4 March 2003

Disney's Princess

Aurora

Ariel

On sale every three weeks

Every girl can be a Princess!

Stories • Colouring • Things

FREE Jumbo spinning top!

NEW

Disney's Puzzle land

Mazes

On sale every month

Packed full of crazy puzzles and activities!

Fun and games with Winnie and friends!

FREE Roo

Disney's Winnie the Pooh

On sale every four week

Autumn activities with Pooh!

Numbers

Published by Egmont Magazines Ltd.

WIN a magical family holiday to DISNEYLAND RESORT PARIS

Imagine a land where the wonderful world of Disney comes alive. Imagine two fantastic Theme Parks: Disneyland® Park, where you'll believe in make-believe and where Disney princes and princesses are real, and Walt Disney Studios® Park, where the magic of Disney meets the fascinating world of movies, television and animation. Come and live the magic at Disneyland® Resort Paris!

For a Disneyland® Resort Paris free brochure call 08705 030303 or visit www.disneylandparis.co.uk

The prize includes:
Return travel for 2 adults and 2 children (aged 3-11), plus 3 nights accommodation at a Disneyland® Resort Paris hotel, including breakfast, and 4 days unlimited admission into the Disneyland® Park and Walt Disney Studios® Park, plus one family character breakfast.

To enter, just answer this simple question:
Which princess had a ball at Disneyland® Resort Paris in February 2003?

Send your answer, along with your name and address on a post card or stuck down envelope to:
Egmont Books Limited
(Disneyland Resort Competition)
239 Kensington High Street
London W8 6SA

The closing date for entries is 23rd January 2004